Vocabulary and Writing 5-6

Contents

How to use this book

What's in this book?

This is one of six books especially devised for children at an early stage in their primary education. Each book has been carefully written to boost children's confidence and to reflect the demands of the National Curriculum.

During Key Stage 1, children are taught to read and write using a variety of approaches, including phonics. They widen their vocabulary and learn an increasing range of spellings, enabling them to begin to express themselves through their writing.

In mathematics, children develop skills in number work as well as in measurement and shape, and make use of these skills as they start to approach mathematical 'problems'. They will begin to learn the two, five and ten times tables.

These books provide a wealth of materials that can help children through this exciting phase of their learning.

How you can help

To begin with, your child may find some of the activities quite tricky, but as they work their way through the book and become more familiar with the types of questions their confidence will grow. Always provide lots of encouragement and explain that they should learn from any mistakes rather than be disheartened.

Children gain confidence by learning facts at home that they can use in their work at school. Help your child by displaying posters on their bedroom wall or around the house, showing facts such as the days of the week and the months of the year.

In each of the books, some questions or tasks are repeated to help your child learn and revise vital facts. Taking the time to discuss the questions with your child and helping to explain anything they find difficult will produce the best results.

Encourage your child to complete only one or two pages at a time. Regular short bursts of practice are more likely to result in long-term progress than long sessions of work. Practising little and often, with lots of well-deserved praise, will help your child to find learning enjoyable. Enjoy the books together!

Notes for parents

Your child has a huge range of spoken vocabulary and will already be building a substantial body of written vocabulary. The lists below show the type of words that they will be acquiring at school in Phases 2 to 5 of their phonics programme.

This book provides practice in using many of these words, together with other related vocabulary, through meaningful written exercises. Enjoy working with your child to help them create beautiful written work.

Phase 2:

a	an	as	at	if	in	is	it	of	off
on	up	am	can	dad	had	and	get	big	him
his	not	got	mum	but	back				

Phase 3:

sat	tap	sit	pit	tip	pip	sip	pan	pin	tin
nap	man	mat	map	dad	sad	dip	did	gap	pig
dig	pot	top	dog	pop	cot	cap	cat	kid	kit
sock	sack	dock	pack	pick	pet	ten	net	pen	peg
men	neck	run	mug	cup	sun	mud	rim	rat	hot
hut	hop	hum	hit	hat	hug	back	bag	bed	bug
bun	bus	bat	bin	fit	fin	fun	fog	puff	huff
cuff	fan	lap	leg	let	bell	fill	doll	tell	sell
hill	mill	dull	full	less	hiss	mess	boss	fuss	kiss
jam	jet	jog	van	vet	win	web	wig	wax	wet
mix	box	six	fox	yes	yet	yell	zip	buzz	quiz
chip	chin	check	such	much	rich	chill	chap	chick	chat
ship	shop	shed	shell	fish	dish	wish	rush	shock	cash
moth	thin	thick	ring	song	wing	rung	king	long	sing
wait	pain	sail	main	tail	rain	feel	feet	jeep	teeth
seem	meet	week	deep	keep	high	light	might	night	tight
coat	goat	loaf	road	soap	boat	zoo	boot	zoom	food
moon	cool	bar	car	bark	card	jar	park	fork	sort
foot	book	cook	good	took	hook	born	worn	torn	cork
burn	curl	hurt	surf	turn	cow	owl	how	town	boil
coin	soil	ear	hear	near	year	hair	fair	sure	cure
join	gear	pair	pure	hammer	letter	ladder	dinner	better	summer

High frequency words

will	that	this	then	them	with	see	for	now	down
look	too	the	to	I	no	go			

Notes for parents

Phase 4:

tent	belt	hump	band	felt	gulp	lamp	wind
nest	sink	best	lift	lost	camp	kept	soft
pond	cost	bank	bunk	hand	next	milk	jump
melt	chest	chimp	bench	thank	shelf	boost	paint
toast	think	burnt	stop	frog	spot	plan	trip
grab	track	spin	flag	twin	sniff	plum	swim
clap	drop	green	fresh	steep	tree	smell	train
spoon	sport	start	trail	cream	clown	star	creep
brown	spark	bring	crash	bleed	swing	float	smart
groan	brush	scoop	frown	droop	clear	growl	thrill
stand	crisp	spend	trust	twist	frost	stamp	blend
grunt	crept	slept	blink	drank	blank	trunk	crunch
shrink	spring	strap	street				

Polysyllabic words

sandpit	windmill	softest	desktop	handstand	lunchbox	sandwich	thundering
starlight	floating	freshness	driftwood	twisting	printer	shampoo	chimpanzee

High frequency words

went	it's	from	children	just	help	he	she we
me	be	was	my	you	her	they	all are

Phase 5:

horse	please	cheese	noise	because	done	nothing	brother
mother	happy	sunny	mummy	daddy	only	donkey	monkey
chimney	money	here	deer	cheer	steering	father	rather
half	calf	where	somewhere	everywhere	care	wear	tear
square	share	all	always	talk	walk	wall	fall
calling	four	your	fourteen	caught	taught	naughty	daughter
learn	earth	early	heard	word	work	world	worm
worse	worst	would	should	pull	push	full	play
spray	crayon	take	game	race	same	snake	sea
bead	read	steam	steamy	these	even	funny	quickly
field	try	tried	cry	cried	dry	dried	fry
fried	why	sky	slide	prize	nice	grow	snow
show	window	toe	goes	home	phone	woke	tune
use	huge	computer	few	new	blue	glue	June
rude	rule	blew	grew	screw	threw	sure	sugar
usual	picture	adventure	nature	mixture	catch	fetch	stitch
kitchen	fudge	hedge	bridge	badge	lamb	climb	crumb
thumb	gnome	sign	knot	knee	knock	know	knew
wrap	wrong	write	listen	castle	house	mouse	

High frequency words

don't	old	I'm	by	time	house	about	your
day	made	came	make	here	saw	very	put
said	have	like	so	do	some	come	were
there	little	one	when	out	what	oh	their
people	Mr	Mrs	looked	called	asked	could	path
bath	ask	fast	last	daft	glass	grass	blast
afternoon							

Pictures and words

man   pig   pin   sock

peg   mug   bed   fox   fish

Look at the pictures. Write the correct word under each picture.

bed   mug   pin

fish   peg   pig

sock   man   fox

Now try this!

Can you write the names of three different items of clothing?

Notes for parents

Can your child match the written words to the pictures? Encourage them to write the words in the correct places using clear handwriting. Help them to think of three different items of clothing and support them in spelling these words correctly.

Words and sentences

man   dog   van   in

sits   the   mug   has   sitting

Look at the picture. What can you see?

Write about the picture. You can use the words above to help.

_____

_____

_____

_____

Now try this!

Look out of your window. Describe what you can see.

Notes for parents

The first activity is to talk about the picture together: where are the man and the dog? What are they both doing? Now talk about the words, helping your child to read each one. In the final activity, help your child to think of one or two sentences to describe what is happening in the picture. Encourage them to form their letters correctly and to leave appropriate spaces between words.

What can you see?

bus   van   jam   box

shell   ship   shed   dish   moth

Look at the pictures. Write the correct word under each picture.

box _____   bus _____

jam _____

Now try this!

Can you write the names of three different toys?

Notes for parents

Can your child match the written words to the pictures? Encourage them to write the words in the correct places using clear handwriting. Help them to think of three different toys and support them in spelling the words correctly.

What can you write?

cook	book	looks	his	in
the	dinner	to	cooking	looking

Look at the picture. What can you see?

Write about the picture.

_____

_____

_____

_____

Now try this!

Can you write the names of your favourite food and drink?

Notes for parents

The first activity is to talk about the picture together. Who is the character in the picture? What is he doing? Now talk about the words, helping your child to read each one. In the final activity, help your child to think of one or two sentences to describe what is happening in the picture. Encourage them to form their letters correctly and to leave appropriate spaces between words.

Creating a rhyme

cat   spotty   frog   long   big   thin

dog   rat   fat   green   small

Complete the sentences using the words above.

Who is there?

A big, fat _____

Who is there?

A long, thin _____

Now write your own full sentences.

Who is there?

_____

Who is there?

_____

Now try this!

Look at a nursery rhyme. Can you find words that rhyme with each other?

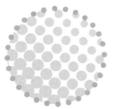

Notes for parents

Talk about the pictures, encouraging your child to use describing words. Can they create a sentence by writing a line for each creature? They may wish to use words that are not included in the list at the top. Once completed, read the four lines and listen to the rhyme together.

Matching pictures and words

hammer · dinner · ladder · tent · nest

sink · milk · frog · flag

Look at the pictures. Write the correct word under each picture.

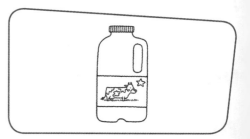

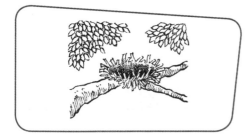

Now try this!

Can you write the names of three different tools?

Notes for parents

Can your child match the written words to the pictures? Encourage them to write the words in the correct places using clear handwriting. Talk about which of the words have two syllables e.g. hammer. Help them to think of three different tools then prompt them with letters for writing them down.

Comparisons

a	Mum	big	hat	has

flowers	flowery	small	tall	bigger	smaller

Look at the picture.

Dad has a small hat.

Write about Mum and her hat.

_____

_____

_____

Now try this!

Write about what you are wearing today.

Notes for parents

Talk about the picture, comparing the two hats. Read the words in the list together and read the short sentence about Dad's hat. Can your child think of a descriptive sentence to write about Mum and her hat?

Write about the picture

sad   looks   toast   toaster   burnt

the   is   in   smoke   bread

loaf   man   spoilt   hungry

Look at the picture.
What can you see?

Write about the picture.

_____

_____

_____

_____

_____

Now try this!

Write about what
the man should do
next.

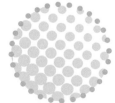

Notes for parents

The first activity is to talk about the picture together. What
has gone wrong? How do you think the man feels? Now
talk about the words, helping your child to read each one.
In the final activity, help your child to think of one or two
sentences to describe what is happening in the picture.
Encourage them to form their letters correctly and to leave
appropriate spaces between words.

Harder words

windmill   handstand   lunchbox   horse

cheese   chimney   calf   square   worm

Look at the pictures. Write the correct word under each picture.

  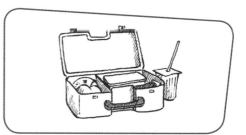

  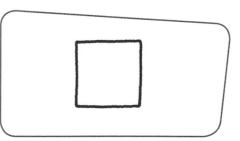

Now try this!

Can you write the names of three different types of buildings?

Notes for parents

Some of the words on this page are tricky to spell. You may like to point out the three compound words: windmill, lunchbox and handstand are each made from two other words joined together. Help them to think of three different types of buildings, and support them as they write them down.

Using words in sentences

chimpanzee   sandpit   does   in

handstand   the   doing   there

Look at the picture. What can you see?

Write about the picture.

_____

_____

_____

_____

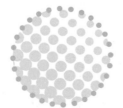

Now try this!

Can you write the names of three different animals?

More matching

calf   walk   fall   daughter

world   snake   steam   slide   window

Look at the pictures. Write the correct word under each picture.

  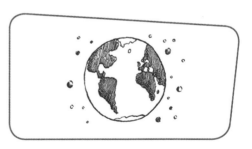

Now try this!

Can you write the names of three different baby animals?

Notes for parents

Can your child match the written words to each picture? Encourage them to write the words in the correct places using clear handwriting. Some of the words are tricky to spell as they include unsounded letters (silent letters). Help them to think of three different baby animals and support them in spelling these words correctly.

Billy Goats Gruff

troll   under   over   on   hiding

billy goat   field   grass   bridge   across

went   was   the   eat   to   some

**Look at the picture.
What can you see?**

Write about the picture.

_____

_____

_____

_____

_____

Now try this!

**What do you think
might happen next
in the story?**

Notes for parents

You may like to remind your child of the story of the Three Billy
Goats Gruff. Which part of the story does the picture show? Discuss
what is going to happen next. If your child feels confident about
this, ask them to write the next part of the story as well.

Days of the week

Read about my week.

On Monday I go to my grandma's house.

On Tuesday I go swimming.

On Wednesday I visit my friend.

On Thursday I have chips for tea.

On Friday I play on the computer.

On Saturday I go shopping.

On Sunday I stay in bed quite late!

Write about your week.

_____

_____

_____

_____

_____

_____

_____

Now try this!

Can you write about a very special day?

Notes for parents

Talk about your child's week: do they enjoy any of the activities listed in the sentences? Help them to compose their own sentences about things they do. Can they think of what they did on a very special day, such as their birthday or a holiday?

Home

house flat bungalow mobile home

caravan road town village city

country garden

Read about the house.

My house is in a village. It is a small house.

There is a tree in the garden.

Write about your home.

_____

_____

_____

_____

_____

_____

Now try this!

Can you write about somebody else's home?

Notes for parents

Talk about the picture and the words. What is your home like? Can the words in the list be used to describe it? Talk about other people your child knows, perhaps grandparents or friends – can your child write about their home?

Pets

budgie   tortoise   horse   guinea pig

goldfish   cat   dog   gerbil

Read about the hamster.

**This is a pet hamster and he is called Rory.
He plays on a wheel in his cage.**

Can you write about this dog?

_____

_____

_____

_____

_____

Now try this!

Write about a
pet you know.

Notes for parents

Read the words and the sentences with your child.
If you have a pet, can your child describe it and the things
it does? If you don't have a pet, talk about a pet belonging to a
friend or neighbour.

Spring

blossom   leaves   tree   flowers   pink

white   red   blue   there   are

growing   spring   dark   light   nest   birds

**Look at the spring picture.
What can you see?**

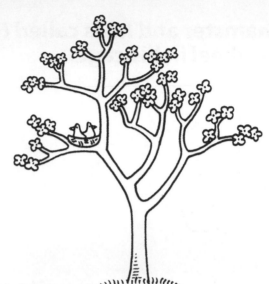

Write about the picture.

_____

_____

_____

_____

_____

_____

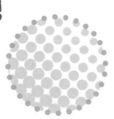

Now try this!

Talk about spring.

Notes for parents

Read the words and talk about the picture with your child. Help them to write some sentences. Do they remember the spring? What do they remember about it? What changes in the spring?

Summer

beach people colours sea sand

red sun-bathing yellow purple orange

playing paddling blue summer hot warm

Look at the summer picture. What can you see?

Write about the picture.

_____

_____

_____

_____

_____

_____

Now try this!

Talk about summer.

Notes for parents

Read the words and talk about the picture with your child. Help them to write some sentences. Do they remember the summer? What do they remember about it? How do they dress in summer? What do they do in the evenings?

Autumn

tree	leaves	red	orange	autumn

blue	turned	have	brown	dark

evenings	colder	darker	fireworks	bonfire

Look at the autumn picture. What can you see?

Write about the picture.

_____

_____

_____

_____

_____

_____

Now try this!

Talk about autumn.

Notes for parents

Read the words and talk about the picture with your child. Help them to write some sentences. Do they remember the autumn? What do they remember about it? Do they watch fireworks? Do they have bonfires?

Winter

snowman   a   this   winter   very   cold

snow   scarf   hat   coal   picture

mouth   nose   is   eyes   legs   arms

Look at the winter picture. What can you see?

Write about the picture.

_____

_____

_____

_____

_____

_____

ow try this!

Talk about winter.

Notes for parents

Read the words and talk about the picture with your child. Help them to write some sentences about the snowman. Do they remember the winter? What do they remember about it? Have they built a snowman before?

Months of the year

Read about some of the things I did last year.

My birthday was in January and I got a new bike.

I ate chocolate eggs in April.

I went on holiday in August.

I watched fireworks in November.

Write about your year.

_____

_____

_____

_____

_____

_____

_____

Now try this!

What would you like to do next year?

Notes for parents

Talk about your family's year. When are family birthdays? What special events took place over the past year? What special events are you looking forward to?